Lincoln Peirce

BiG NATE

HERE GOES NOTHING

HarperCollins *Children's Books*

First published in Great Britain by HarperCollins *Children's Books* in 2012
HarperCollins *Children's Books* is a division of HarperCollins*Publishers* Ltd,
1 London Bridge Street, London SE1 9GF

These comic strips first appeared in newspapers between
9th June 2008 and 10th January 2009.

The HarperCollins website address is: www.harpercollins.co.uk

Text and illustration copyright © 2012 United Feature Syndicate, Inc.

ISBN 978-0-00-747832-3

The author asserts the moral right to be identified as the author of the work.

Printed and bound by CPI Group (UK) Ltd, Croydon, CR0 4YY

MIX
Paper from
responsible sources
FSC FSC C007454

More

adventures from

Lincoln Peirce

Novels:

BIG NATE: THE BOY WITH THE BIGGEST HEAD IN THE WORLD

BIG NATE STRIKES AGAIN

BIG NATE ON A ROLL

BIG NATE GOES FOR BROKE

Activity Books:

BIG NATE BOREDOM BUSTER

BIG NATE FUN BLASTER

Comic Compilations:

BIG NATE: WHAT COULD POSSIBLY GO WRONG?

THE SHOW
MUST GO ON

YOU GUYS CAN MAKE FUN OF ME FOR MY STAGE FRIGHT, BUT YOU WOULDN'T BE LAUGHING IF IT HAD HAPPENED TO **YOU**!

IT WAS **HORRIFYING**! I JUST **FROZE** UP THERE! IT WAS LIKE BEING **PARALYSED**!

MY MIND WAS A TOTAL **BLANK**! I'VE NEVER EXPERIENCED THAT BEFORE!

NOT EVEN ON LAST WEEK'S SOCIAL STUDIES TEST?

...WHEN YOU IDENTIFIED APPOMATTOX AS THE GREEK GOD OF CREME-FILLED PASTRIES?

© 2008 by NEA, Inc.

WHAT ARE YOU DOING?

ME? NOTHIN'.

SHOULDN'T YOU BE STUDYING?

STUDYING FOR **WHAT**?

FINALS WERE **LAST** WEEK! THERE'S NOTHING LEFT TO STUDY FOR!

THE NEXT COUPLE DAYS OF SCHOOL ARE JUST **MAKE-UPS** FOR THE **SNOW DAYS** WE HAD!

IT'S NOT LIKE ANYTHING **HAPPENS!** ALL WE DO IS EMPTY OUT OUR LOCKERS AND CLEAN THE CLASSROOMS!

CLEAN THE CLASSROOMS, EH?

YUP

I DON'T THINK YOU'RE READY FOR THAT. YOU'D BETTER PRACTISE.

HARDY HAR **HAR**.

© 2008 by NEA, Inc.

PRANKED!

LAST DAY OF SCHOOL, LADDIES! **PRANK DAY!**

DON'T BE SO SURE, NATE. REMEMBER WHAT PRINCIPAL NICHOLS SAID AT THE ASSEMBLY LAST WEEK?

THEY'RE CRACKING DOWN THIS YEAR! THEY WANT THE SCHOOL TO BE A PRANK-FREE ZONE!

OH COME **ON,** TEDDY! THEY SAY THAT **EVERY** YEAR!

DO THEY REALLY EXPECT US TO TAKE THEM SERIOUS~.....

....LY?

MORNING.

AH! PRINCIPAL NICHOLS! HEY, I JUST WANTED TO SAY: GOOD TRY!

I MEAN, POSTING A BOGUS COP OUTSIDE THE SCHOOL ON "PRANK DAY"? THAT **SHOWED** ME SOMETHING! THAT TOLD ME YOU'RE A **PLAYER!**

6/20

IT DIDN'T **WORK**, OF COURSE, BUT THAT'S ALL PART OF THE GIVE-AND-TAKE! YOU TRY TO PLAY PRANKS ON **US**, **WE** TRY TO PLAY PRANKS ON **YOU!**

© 2008 by NEA, Inc.

SIR? THERE'S A LOCUST SWARM IN THE TEACHERS' LOUNGE.

WELL, I SEE YOU'RE BUSY! TOODLES!

HEY, GUYS, I WAS JUST THINKING...

YOU KNOW HOW WHEN WE GO BACK TO SCHOOL IN THE FALL, WE'VE FORGOTTEN EVERYTHING WE LEARNED THE YEAR BEFORE?

WELL, WE COULD **PREVENT** THAT FROM HAPPENING BY FORMING OUR OWN LITTLE **STUDY GROUP** THIS SUMMER!

IF WE SPEND JUST A HALF-HOUR EACH DAY REVIEWING OUR SCHOOL-WORK, IT'LL ALL BE FRESH IN OUR MINDS COME SEPTEMBER!

A SUMMER STUDY GROUP?

RIGHT!

AND HOW DID YOU COME UP WITH THIS IDEA?

WELL, I... HEY, WHO REALLY **KNOWS** WHERE GREAT IDEAS COME FROM?

IT JUST... **HIT** ME!

DIFF!

THE SUMMER
OF NATE

IT'S GREAT THAT IT'S SUMMER AND EVERYTHING, BUT I WANT **MORE!** I WANT THIS TO BE THE BEST SUMMER **EVER!**

YOU KNOW WHAT THIS SUMMER NEEDS? IT NEEDS SOME **BUZZ!** IT NEEDS A HIP, EXCITING **THEME!**

A THEME?

SOMETHING LIKE "SUMMER 2008: FEEL THE HEAT!"

THAT SOUNDS LIKE A PUBLIC SERVICE ANNOUNCEMENT FOR GLOBAL WARMING.

HOW ABOUT "SUMMER 2008: THEMES ARE LAME!"

HERE'S A GOOD THEME: "2008: THE SUMMER OF NATE!"

...OR "SUMMER '08: GET READY FOR TEDDY!"

NOTHING RHYMES WITH FRANCIS.

Peirce

HOW CAN WE MAKE OURSELVES SOME MONEY THIS SUMMER, GUYS?

WE COULD START UP OUR YARD CARE BUSINESS AGAIN!

NO! NO MORE YARD CARE STUFF! THAT'S JUST **DRUDGE** WORK! I WANT TO DO SOMETHING WHERE I CAN BE **CREATIVE**!

I CAN'T DEMONSTRATE MY CREATIVITY BY DOING **YARD WORK**!

...THOUGH LORD KNOWS, YOU'VE TRIED.

YEAH, REMEMBER YOUR HEDGE-TRIMMING FIASCO AT MRS MULGREW'S?

IT'S CALLED "TOPIARY," LADDIES.

6 25

Peirce

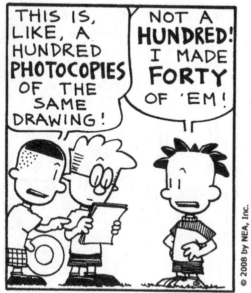

NO, NO, **NO!** **CUT!**

YOU GUYS CALL THIS A **FIGHT SCENE?** THIS IS **HORRIBLE!** I'VE SEEN MORE ACTION IN A GAME OF **TIC-TAC-TOE!**

TEDDY, YOU'RE SUPPOSED TO BE A **DERANGED KILLER!** FRANCIS, YOU'RE SUPPOSED TO BE LOCKED IN A **LIFE AND DEATH STRUGGLE!**

HOW DO YOU EXPECT ME TO MAKE A GOOD PSYCHO SLASHER FILM WITHOUT ANY **PSYCHO SLASHING** GOING ON??

THE AUDIENCE DOESN'T WANT TO WATCH YOU GUYS ACT LIKE YOU'RE AT A **TEA PARTY!** THEY WANT TO SEE **VIOLENCE!**

VIOLENCE! GIVE ME **VIOLENCE!**

WHA-?... **HEY!** WHAT ARE YOU GUYS..? **NO!!** **OW!!**

YOU KNOW, THIS ACTING STUFF AIN'T SO BAD!

YEAH, BUT WHAT I REALLY WANT TO DO IS DIRECT!

WILD RIDE

ONLY TWO PER CAR, KID! TWO'S THE LIMIT!

OH. OK, I'LL JUST RIDE ALONE IN THAT ONE, THEN.

KID, I'VE GOT A LINE HERE THAT'S A MILE LONG! I CAN'T WASTE A SEAT BY GIVING YOU A CAR ALL TO YOUR-SELF!

WE'LL JUST HOOK YOU UP WITH ANOTHER SINGLE!

SINGLE RIDERS! ANY SINGLES?

I'M A SCREAMER!

GREAT.

HOW'D THE "DEATH SPIRAL" TREAT YOU, MY MAN? YOU A LITTLE QUEASY? A BIT WOOZY?

I... I'M OK, I THINK.

AH! YOU'RE ONE OF THE **LUCKY** ONES, THEN! NOT LIKE A KID WHO TRIED TO RIDE THIS BAD BOY **YESTERDAY!**

THE DUDE HAD JUST POUNDED DOWN TWO OR THREE CORN DOGS AND A PINT OF CLAM BELLIES! **THAT** LUNCH CAME BACK UP IN A HURRY, BELIEVE YOU **ME!**

OOLP!

THAT'S WHY I KEEP A HOSE HANDY, KID. THIS HOSE IS MY FRIEND.

© 2008 by NEA, Inc.

THERE'S TONS OF PEOPLE HERE WE KNOW! I SAW JEFF AND NICK AND EMILY AND JENNY AND...

JENNY? YOU SAW JENNY?

DID YOU TALK TO HER? WHAT DID SHE SAY? DID SHE SAY ANYTHING ABOUT ME? DID SHE ASK ABOUT ME AT ALL?

WHAT DID YOU TELL HER? DID YOU TELL HER I SAID HELLO? WHERE WAS SHE? WAS SHE AT THE TEACUPS RIDE, OR THE HI-FLYER, OR...

ONLY 3 TICKETS!

SHE WAS GOING INTO THE "TUNNEL OF LOVE" WITH ARTUR.

OF COURSE SHE WAS.

"SEE A PENNY, PICK IT UP, AND ALL THE DAY YOU'LL HAVE GOOD LUCK!"

HOLD IT!

WHAT?

IS IT HEADS OR TAILS?

WHAT DIFFERENCE DOES **THAT** MAKE?

A PENNY'S ONLY GOOD LUCK IF IT'S **HEADS!**

IF IT'S **TAILS**, IT'S **BAD** LUCK! DON'T TOUCH IT!

SO I'M JUST SUPPOSED TO LEAVE **FREE MONEY** LYING ON THE GROUND? I THINK **NOT!** I'M PICKING IT UP!

AND BY THE WAY, FRANCIS... IT WAS **TAILS!**

KRAK!

WONK!

© 2008 by NEA, Inc.

OOH! HEADS UP!

WHAT BAD LUCK?

YOU'VE GOT NO CHANCE TODAY, WRIGHT! WE'RE GOING TO **CRUSH** YOU GUYS!

OUR TEAM BATTING AVERAGE IS .348, OUR O.B.P. IS .510, AND OUR SLUGGING PERCENTAGE IS .883!

OUR PITCHER IS 6'6" AND WEIGHS THREE HUNDRED POUNDS.

THERE ARE STATS, AND THEN THERE ARE VITAL STATS.

© 2008 by NEA, Inc.

CHESTER! YOU'RE MOWIN' 'EM DOWN OUT THERE! YOU'VE GOT A NO-HITTER GOING!

YOU'RE NOT SUPPOSED TO DO THAT.

YOU'RE NOT SUPPOSED TO MENTION A NO-HITTER WHILE THE GAME'S GOING ON. IT'S BAD LUCK.

BAD LUCK? **WHAT** BAD LUCK? I DON'T SEE ANY BAD LUCK!

ACTUALLY, IT'S HARD TO SEE MUCH OF ANYTHING FROM HERE.

© 2008 by NEA, Inc.

© 2008 by NEA, Inc.

HUNGRY FOR VICTORY

DO YOU EVER PRETEND TO BE A MAJOR LEAGUER WHEN YOU'RE IN THE OUTFIELD?

DO YOU EVER DO PLAY-BY-PLAY IN YOUR HEAD? LIKE, "HERE'S JEFF FRANCOEUR OF THE ATLANTA BRAVES IN RIGHT FIELD..."

NO, I NEVER DO THAT.

THAT MAKES SENSE.

...BECAUSE WHEN A BALL'S HIT TO JEFF FRANCOEUR, HE'S GENERALLY NOT BUSY BUYING A HOT DOG AT THE SNACK BAR.

I WAS HUNGRY. SO SUE ME.

© 2008 by NEA, Inc.

DOUBLE DATE

I CAN ONLY PLAY ANOTHER TEN MINUTES. SHEILA AND I ARE GOING TO A MOVIE.

OOH! I'LL CALL JENNY! WE'LL DOUBLE DATE!

DOUBLE **WHAT**? NATE, JENNY'S GOING **STEADY** WITH **ARTUR**!

DO WE **KNOW** THAT? ARE WE **SURE**?

THEY WERE GOING STEADY A **WEEK** AGO, BUT **ANY-**THING COULD HAVE HAP-PENED SINCE THEN! MAYBE THEY HAD A FIGHT! MAYBE THEY **HATE** EACH OTHER NOW! MAYBE ARTUR **DIED** IN SOME SORT OF HIDEOUS **ACCIDENT**!

7/15

IN OTHER WORDS, ASSUME THE BEST.

RIGHT! I'M A "GLASS-HALF-FULL" KIND OF GUY.

SPECIAL DELIVERY

DESTINATION VACATION

FAMILY
(DYS)FUNCTION

AH! THE HOUSE PAINTER HAS ARRIVED!

HI, GRAMPS.

PUT 'ER THERE! HA HA HA HA!

HA HA. OK.

OH, I'M JUST PULLING YOUR LEG, SON! YOU WON'T BE NEEDING THIS BRUSH RIGHT AWAY!

© 2008 by NEA, Inc.

FIRST YOU'LL NEED TO SCRAPE!

GREAT.

SO LONG, NATE! DO A GOOD JOB FOR GRAMPS!

DON'T WORRY, I WON'T WORK HIM TOO HARD!

YOU CAN WORK HIM AS HARD AS YOU LIKE, DAD! IT'LL DO HIM GOOD TO BREAK A SWEAT!

7/25

HE NEEDS TO GET A LITTLE EXERCISE, BURN A FEW CALORIES!

© 2008 by NEA, Inc.

...SAID THE MAN WHO'LL SUCK DOWN TWO ECLAIRS AND A FRAPPUCCINO ON THE DRIVE HOME.

UP YOU GO! LOOK OUT FOR THE HORNETS' NEST!

GRAB A SCRAPER, UNCLE TED.

WHY ARE WE PAINT-ING THE **OUT**SIDE OF THE HOUSE?

THERE ARE SEVERAL ROOMS **IN**SIDE THE HOUSE IN **DESPERATE** NEED OF ATTENTION!

FOR INSTANCE: WHY WON'T MOTHER AND FATHER HAVE **MY** ROOM PAINTED?

SHK! SHK! SHK!

© 2008 by NEA, Inc.

7/28

BECAUSE THEY'RE WAITING FOR YOU TO MOVE OUT.

I TRIED THAT ONCE. THE COLLEGE DORM WAS A COLD, CRUEL PLACE.

UNCLE TED, ARE YOU GOING TO LET ME PAINT THIS WHOLE HOUSE BY MY**SELF**?

MY BOY, YOU'RE DOING GREAT WITH**OUT** MY HELP!

AND BESIDES, I HAVE TO CONFESS TO BEING A BIT OF A KLUTZ! I'VE NEVER EXACTLY BEEN "HANDY," IF YOU GET MY DRIFT!

I PROBABLY WOULDN'T EVEN KNOW WHAT TO **DO** WITH A PAINT BRUSH!

8/1

© 2008 by NEA, Inc.

GIVE THAT ONE A TRY.

UNCLE TED, HOW ABOUT HELPING ME PAINT?

I'M AFRAID I CAN'T RISK IT, DEAR BOY.

"RISK IT"?

HOLDING A PAINT BRUSH FOR COUNTLESS HOURS COULD DO **MAJOR** DAMAGE TO MY DIGITS!

...AND IF **THAT** HAPPENS, I MAY NEVER PLAY THE OBOE AGAIN!

YOU QUIT THE OBOE IN FIFTH GRADE, TED.

YES, BUT I'M SENS-ING THAT MY MUSE WILL SOON REAWAKEN.

© 2008 by NEA, Inc.

8/6

GRAMPS, UNCLE TED ISN'T HELPING WITH THE PAINTING!

I'VE ASKED HIM **NICELY**, I'VE TRIED TO **GUILT** HIM, I'VE TRIED TO **FORCE** HIM TO HELP!

...BUT HE KEEPS COMING UP WITH ALL THESE LAME EXCUSES NOT TO DO ANY WORK!

WELCOME TO MY WORLD, SON.

I NEED TO LIE DOWN. I FEEL A TOUCH OF MALARIA COMING ON.

BOOP BOOP
BOOP BOOP
BOOP BOOP
BOOP

Hello and thank you for calling Channel 12 Action News. The person you are trying to reach...

...CHIEF METEOROLOGIST *WINK SUMMERS*...

...is not available. Please leave a message. ⁂BEEP!⁂

HELLO, WINK? NATE WRIGHT HERE!

8/3

LISTEN, WINK, I CAUGHT YOUR FORECAST LAST NIGHT, AND I HEARD YOU SAY THAT TODAY'S GOING TO BE A BEAUTIFUL DAY.

IN FACT, YOU SAID THE WHOLE **WEEK'S** GOING TO BE NICE: WARM AND SUNNY, NO CLOUDS, A GENTLE BREEZE...

I BELIEVE YOUR EXACT QUOTE WAS: "PERFECT SUMMER WEATHER FOR **ANY** KIND OF OUT-DOOR ACTIVITY"!

AND YOU KNOW WHAT? YOU NAILED IT! YOUR FORE-CAST WAS 100% ACCURATE!

YOU'RE KILLING ME, WINK.

LET'S GO, SON! THIS HOUSE WON'T PAINT ITSELF!

© 2008 by NEA, Inc.

60

THIS IS GOING TO BE EPIC!

TEDDY, TOSS THE BALL JUST AS I'M HITTING THE TRAMPOLINE!

RIGHT!

I'LL THROW DOWN A TOMAHAWK DUNK FOR THE MOST SPECTACULAR ALLEY-OOP IN SPORTS HISTORY!

8/10

...AND FRANCIS, GET THE WHOLE THING ON VIDEO! WE'LL PUT THIS PUPPY ON YOUTUBE!

WE'RE ROLLING!

OKAY, THEN! HERE WE GO!!

ALLEY!...

CLANNG!

© 2008 by NEA, Inc.

...OOP.

WE CAN STILL PUT THIS ON YOUTUBE, BUT INSTEAD OF "SPORTS", WE'LL POST IT UNDER "COMEDY."

Peirce

IT'S PRETTY AWESOME THAT GRAMPS GAVE ME FIVE HUNDRED DOLLARS FOR MY COLLEGE FUND...

...BUT I WON'T BE ABLE TO **USE** THAT MONEY FOR **YEARS!** I DIDN'T EARN ANY **MONEY** MONEY! I DIDN'T EARN ANY **NOW** MONEY!

I PAINTED THAT WHOLE HOUSE! I WORKED MY BUTT OFF AND I HAVE NOTHING TO SHOW FOR IT!

...AND THEN HE SORT OF SMILED AND SAID, "WELCOME TO THE REAL WORLD".

I HATE WHEN THEY DO THAT.

Peirce

NOTHING
TO DO

"YOU ARE THE MASTER OF EVERY SITUATION"! NOW **THAT'S** A GOOD HOROSCOPE!

WHOA, WHOA! **HOLD** IT!

FIVE **SECONDS** AGO, YOU SAID THAT HOROSCOPES ARE **STUPID!** NOW YOU GET A **GOOD** ONE, AND ALL OF THE SUDDEN YOU'RE GOING TO PAY ATTENTION?

8/19

WHAT HAPPENED TO ALL THAT STUFF ABOUT HOROSCOPES BEING **BOGUS?**

MOST OF THEM **ARE!**

© 2008 by NEA, Inc.

...BUT THIS ONE REALLY CAPTURES MY ESSENCE.

YES, I CAN SMELL IT FROM HERE.

Peirce

OK, WHAT SHOULD I TRY FIRST?

WHATTA YA MEAN?

FRANCIS, I JUST GOT A HOROSCOPE TELLING ME I'M THE MASTER OF EVERY SITUATION! I SHOULD BE ABLE TO TRY JUST ABOUT ANYTHING AND DO IT **PERFECTLY!**

8/20

I'LL JUST WANDER DOWN THE BEACH AND FIND SOME RANDOM SITUATION TO MASTER!

© 2008 by NEA, Inc.

SORRY I'M LATE! WHAT'S UP?

NOT MUCH. NATE'S ACTING LIKE A MORON, THAT'S ALL.

HIS HOROSCOPE SAID HE'S THE MASTER OF ANY SITUATION, SO NOW HE'S WALKING UP AND DOWN THE BEACH LOOKING FOR SITUATIONS TO MASTER!

8/22

WHAT KIND OF SITUATIONS?

I BELIEVE AT THE MOMENT IT'S BEACH VOLLEYBALL.

© 2008 by NEA, Inc.

OK, HEADS UP, EVERY- ONE.

JUST GIVE ME THE BALL, KID.

BUY BYE

NATE, THE FIVE BUCKS I GAVE YOU WERE FOR **SCHOOL SUPPLIES**, NOT **ICE CREAM!**

NOW GET YOURSELF BACK TO THE STORE, AND BUY SOME SCHOOL SUPPLIES WITH YOUR **OWN** MONEY!

BUT I DON'T **HAVE** MY OWN MONEY!

IF I **DID** HAVE MY OWN MONEY, I WOULDN'T HAVE NEEDED TO ASK **YOU** FOR MONEY TO BUY SCHOOL SUPPLIES!

BUT YOU **DIDN'T** BUY SCHOOL SUPPLIES!

DAD, YOU'RE GETTING OFF TOPIC. THE POINT IS, CAN I HAVE SOME MONEY?

NATE! WHAT'S UP?

OH, I'M ON MY WAY TO "OFFICE MART".

whut

KLASSIC KOMIX

MY DAD'S MAKING ME BUY SCHOOL SUPPLIES.

WHAT? YOU CAN BUY THAT STUFF **ANYTIME!**

... BUT THE NEW ISSUE OF "FEMME FATALITY" WILL BE **SOLD OUT** WITHIN THE **HOUR!**

8/28

WELL, THEN, SCHOOL SUPPLIES BE **HANGED!**

KA-CHING!

KLASSIC KO

MOULD!

WHAT'S ALL THIS ABOUT MOULD, TEDDY?

IT'S ALL OVER THE SCHOOL! IT'S POISONING THE AIR!

THEY'VE GOT TO CLEAN IT ALL UP! IT'S GOING TO DELAY THE START OF CLASSES!

THEY SAY THAT SPENDING TIME IN THE SCHOOL BUILDING IS MAKING PEOPLE SICK!

BUT HEY, TELL US SOMETHING WE **DIDN'T** KNOW!

HEARD THAT!

© 2008 by NEA, Inc.

IS IT TRUE, DAD? IS IT TRUE?

IT'S TRUE, ALL RIGHT! I JUST TALKED WITH THE HEAD OF THE SCHOOL BOARD!

THEY WERE GETTING THE BUILDING READY FOR THE START OF CLASSES, AND THEY DISCOVERED TOXIC MOULD!

9/3

WHERE DID THE TOXIC MOULD **COME** FROM?

NOBODY KNOWS!

© 2008 by NEA, Inc.

MAY I SUGGEST NATE'S LOCKER AS A LIKELY SOURCE?

OOH! **YES!** THAT THING IS A GIANT **PETRI DISH!**

IT'S BACK-TO-SCHOOL TIME FOR LOCAL CHILDREN... BUT NOT FOR THE STUDENTS AT ONE OF THE CITY'S OLDEST SCHOOLS.

GUYS!

MOULD WAS DISCOVERED THIS WEEK AT PUBLIC SCHOOL #38, EARNING THE BUILDING A DESIGNATION AS A LEVEL-FOUR HEALTH RISK.

CLEAN-UP EFFORTS HAVE BEGUN, BUT OFFICIALS WILL NOT COMMENT ON THE TIMETABLE FOR COMPLETION. FOR NOW, THEY ARE SAYING ONLY THAT THE SCHOOL WILL REMAIN CLOSED "INDEFINITELY".

UP NEXT: MEET A WACKY PARROT WHO SINGS OPERA!

INDEFINITELY!

WOW! LOOK AT **THIS,** GUYS! THEY'VE GOT **TAPE** ALL AROUND THE SCHOOL! IT'S **QUARANTINED!**

IT'S WEIRD SEEING IT LIKE THIS, ISN'T IT? I MEAN, WE SHOULD BE **IN** THERE! IT SHOULD BE FILLED WITH **KIDS!**

$\frac{9}{8}$

IT'S SAD.

OH, YES. VERY SAD.

...BUT SOMEHOW, I'LL MANAGE TO SMILE THROUGH THE TEARS!

I'LL **DANCE!**

HOW COME YOU GUYS ARE SO UPSET ABOUT GOING TO SCHOOL AT JEFFERSON?

DAD! JEFFERSON IS OUR ARCH-RIVAL!

BUT IT'S SUCH A NICE BUILDING! IT'S SO MODERN AND CLEAN!

EXACTLY! THEIR SCHOOL IS A PALACE! THEY THINK THEY'RE BETTER THAN US!

...AND NOW WE'VE GOT TO BEG THEM TO SPARE US A FEW STINKIN' CLASSROOMS BECAUSE OUR SCHOOL HAS MOULD!

MAYBE, LIKE MOULD, THEY'LL... ✳ HA HA! ✳... GROW ON YOU!

NICE, DAD. WAY TO MAKE LIGHT OF OUR SHAME.

Peirce

WELL! GOOD MORNING, SLEEPYHEAD! HOW'RE YOU FEELING? READY FOR YOUR BIG DAY?

BIG DAY?

YOUR FIRST DAY AT JEFFERSON! ARE YOU EXCITED? MAYBE A LITTLE NERVOUS?

NERVOUS? WHY? IT'S JUST A SCHOOL!

9/15

THE JEFFERSON KIDS ARE NO DIFFERENT THAN **I** AM! THEY PUT THEIR PANTS ON ONE LEG AT A TIME JUST LIKE **I** DO!

© 2008 by NEA, Inc.

SOUNDS LIKE QUITE A PLACE.

HM?

Peirce

LUCKY, LUCKIER, LUCKIEST

WHERE SHOULD I SIT, MR... UHHH...?

I'M MR CHUNG!

I'M PUTTING YOU OVER BY THE BOOKCASE, NATE, WITH TWO OF YOUR P.S. 38 CLASSMATES.

CLASSMATES? WHICH ONES?

UH... CHESTER BUDRICK AND GINA HEMPHILL.

OK, JUST A WORD TO THE WISE: GINA'S A TOTAL SUCK-UP.

© 2008 by NEA, Inc.

WELL, THANK YOU, NATE, I'LL KEEP THAT IN...

AND CHESTER'S A PSYCHO. TRY NOT TO MAKE EYE CONTACT.

UGH! NO-BODY TOLD ME THIS WAS A **REMEDIAL** CLASS!

SAVE YOUR BREATH, GINA! EVEN **YOU** CAN'T ANNOY ME TODAY!

I'M BASKING IN THE GLOW OF FINDING OUT WE'VE GOT **MR CHUNG** INSTEAD OF MRS GODFREY!

9/25

MR CHUNG LOOKS LIKE HE'S BARELY OUT OF **HIGH SCHOOL!** I'LL BET HE'S A **LIGHT-WEIGHT!** A REAL **PUSHOVER!**

MR CHUNG? NATE JUST CALLED YOU A PUSH-OVER.

OK, NOW YOU'RE STARTING TO ASCEND "MOUNT ANNOYING."

ALL RIGHT, PEOPLE... AS YOU KNOW, THE STUDENTS FROM P.S. 38 WILL BE ATTENDING **OUR** SCHOOL FOR A WHILE!

WE'RE DELIGHTED THAT THREE OF THEM ARE JOINING US IN FIRST PERIOD SOCIAL STUDIES: CHESTER, GINA, AND NATE!

PLEASE MAKE THEM FEEL WELCOME! SHOW THEM AROUND! BE FRIENDLY!

HELLOOO, FRIEND!

HOO, BOY.

HOW LONG ARE YOU GONNA BE HERE?

THEY'RE STILL NOT SURE!

IT ALL DEPENDS ON HOW LONG IT TAKES THEM TO CLEAN UP THE MOULD! WE MIGHT BE BACK IN OUR OWN SCHOOL BY NOVEMBER, OR IT MIGHT TAKE UNTIL **CHRISTMAS!**

9/30

I WAS TALKING ABOUT THE TABLE, GENIUS. THAT'S **OUR** TABLE.

© 2008 by NEA, Inc.

HOW LONG ARE YOU GONNA BE HERE?

WE WERE JUST LEAVING.

WOW! MR ROSA! IS THIS WHERE YOU GET TO TEACH ART?

YUP! ISN'T THIS GREAT?

THIS IS THE NICEST STUDIO I'VE EVER SEEN IN A MIDDLE SCHOOL! THESE JEFFERSON STUDENTS ARE LUCKY TO HAVE SUCH A FACILITY!

IT'S NOT TURNING THEM INTO GOOD ARTISTS, THOUGH. I MEAN, THAT PAINTING IS **HIDEOUS!**

10/1

THAT'S MINE, SON.

HIDEOUS IN A **GOOD** WAY.

AH! JENNY, M'LADY!

"PALM READING"?

WHAT DO **YOU** KNOW ABOUT PALM READING?

A LOT! I GOT A BOOK ABOUT IT!

PALM $1

FORGET IT. THIS IS JUST ANOTHER ONE OF YOUR RIP-OFFS.

NO! WAIT!

I'LL READ YOUR PALM FOR **FREE**!

FREE?

PALM READING $1

EXACTLY! IF IT'S **FREE**, IT CAN'T BE A RIP-OFF, RIGHT?

I GUESS NOT...

OK, THEN! HERE WE GO!

PALM READING $1

MM-HM... MMM-HMM... MMMMMMM...

PALM READING $1

THIS COSTS TOO MUCH.

ROWR!

COACH, HOW'S SOCCER GOING TO WORK? ARE WE GOING TO PLAY ON THE SAME TEAM WITH THE JEFFERSON KIDS, OR..?

NO, IT'LL BE JUST LIKE ANY OTHER YEAR!

JUST BECAUSE WE'RE SHARING THEIR **BUILDING** DOESN'T MEAN WE'RE JOINING THEIR **TEAM!** THEY HAVE **THEIR** SQUAD...

...AND WE HAVE **OURS!**

...SUCH AS IT IS...

MY BAD.

119

AH! **GOALIE!** I HAVE A PICTURE TO SHOW YOU FROM OUR **YEARBOOK!**

SEE? THAT'S **ME**, SCORING A GOAL! AND THAT'S **YOU**, FLOPPING AROUND ON YOUR **STOMACH!**

THERE'LL BE A LOT **MORE** OF THAT WHEN WE PLAY YOU LADIES NEXT WEEK!

HEH HEH! HA! HA HA HA!

WE GOTTA WIN THIS GAME.

Peirce

THE CAPTAIN OF THE JEFFERSON TEAM KEEPS TRASH-TALKING ME! I'M GONNA SERVE HIM UP A STEAMING PLATE OF **SMACK**!

NO, NATE!

WE'RE **GUESTS** HERE AT JEFFERSON! I DON'T WANT ANY OF OUR STUDENTS CONTRIBUTING TO A **CONFLICT**!

DON'T GET DRAGGED DOWN TO HIS LEVEL, NATE! BE THE BIGGER MAN!

...WHICH ISN'T EASY TO DO WHEN YOU'RE ONLY 4'6"!

YOU'RE NOT HELPING.

PAT PAT!

ALL RIGHT, BOYS, WE'VE GOT A BIG JOB TO DO TODAY. JEFFERSON IS A FORMIDABLE OPPONENT.

PLEA
PUT A
YOU
EQUIPM

COACH

...BUT THEY'RE **BEAT-ABLE!** GUYS, WE'RE **VERY** CAPABLE OF WINNING THIS GAME!

RIGHT! WHO **CARES** THAT THEY'VE WON THEIR GAMES BY A COMBINED SCORE OF 89-3?

10/17

PLEASE PUT AWAY YOUR EQUIPME

COACH

© 2008 by NEA, Inc.

TIMING, SON. TIMING.

WHAT DID I TELL YOU ABOUT THE STATS?

OK, MEN! TIME TO TAKE THE FIELD!

COACH, CAN I LEAD US IN A PRAYER FIRST?

A PRAYER? NATE, WE'VE NEVER HAD A TEAM PRAYER BEFORE.

BUT THIS IS **BIG**, COACH! THIS IS THE BIGGEST GAME OF OUR **LIVES!**

THEY SAY WE SHOULDN'T EVEN PLAY AGAINST THEIR SOCCER TEAM TODAY. THEY TELL US THAT WE CAN'T COMPETE AGAINST THEIR SQUAD, SO SWIFT AND FLEET. THEY MOCK US, TAUNT US, CALL US LAME, THEY LAUGH AND SAY WE'VE GOT NO GAME.

© 2008 by NEA, Inc.

I DON'T KNOW IF THIS PRAYER STUFF WORKS, BUT LORD, PLEASE HELP US SMOKE THESE JERKS.

AMEN!

RULE 7.2 If the score is tied at the conclusion of a 70-minute match, a ten-minute overtime period is played.

RULE 7.3 If at the conclusion of the overtime period no winner has been determined, the outcome of the match is decided by a series of penalty kicks.

FORMAT Five players from each side are selected by their respective coaches to take penalty kicks in alternating order.

The team that successfully converts more penalty kicks than its opponent is declared the winner.

144

COACH! TO CELEBRATE OUR BIG WIN, CAN WE GO OUT FOR PIZZA?

I'M AFRAID NOT, NATE.

HOW 'BOUT ICE CREAM? CAN WE GO OUT FOR ICE CREAM?

SORRY. THAT'S NOT IN THE BUDGET.

...BUT WE **DO** HAVE SOME BEEF JERKY LEFT OVER FROM LAST SEASON!

THE THRILL OF VICTORY.

THE AGONY OF THE MEAT.

CHECK IT OUT, NATE! FRONT PAGE OF THE SPORTS SECTION! "P.S. 38 SHOCKS JEFFERSON"!

OOH! READ IT!

"IN A STUNNING UPSET, THE BOYS' SOCCER TEAM FROM P.S. 38 ENDED JEFFERSON MIDDLE SCHOOL'S FOUR-YEAR UNBEATEN STREAK YESTERDAY WITH A THRILLING 1-0 WIN DECIDED BY PENALTY KICKS."

"THE OUTCOME WAS IN DOUBT UNTIL JEFFERSON'S FINAL SHOOTER, STAR STRIKER ZACK BELFOUR, WAS ROBBED ON A SPECTACULAR SAVE BY P.S. 38 GOALKEEPER MATE WRIGHT."

"MATE WRIGHT"?

THAT SOUNDS DIRTY.

UH-OH.

I'LL HANDLE THIS.

HEY! FOOTBALL! GOT ROOM FOR ONE MORE?

UH... I DON'T THINK SO.

WE'VE ALREADY GOT OUR TEAMS: FOUR GUYS, TWO-ON-TWO.

10/12

FIVE GUYS WON'T WORK?

NO, IT ONLY WORKS WITH AN EVEN NUMBER.

OK, THEN.

SORRY, DAD!

NOW... WHERE WERE WE?

MR EUSTIS WANTS IN! NOW WE'VE GOT AN EVEN NUMBER!

© 2008 by NEA, Inc.

"I'LL HANDLE THIS".

SHUT UP.

CAN I BE QUARTERBACK?

Peirce

RAKE AWAY, SUCKERS!

SUCKERS?

WE'RE BEING **PAID!** HOW DOES THAT MAKE US SUCKERS?

YOU'RE WORKING TOO **HARD**, THAT'S HOW!

I'VE FOUND A **BETTER** WAY TO EARN A LITTLE CASH!

YOU'VE SEEN MY DOG-WALKING FLIERS ALL OVER THE NEIGHBOURHOOD? WELL, SOME LADY OVER ON ELM STREET JUST CALLED ME UP AND **HIRED** ME!

WHILE **YOU** GUYS ARE EARNING FIVE DOLLARS AN HOUR, **I'LL** BE MAKING **TEN** BUCKS FOR TAKING A 20-MINUTE STROLL AROUND THE BLOCK!

THIS WILL BE THE EASIEST MONEY I EVER MADE IN MY **LIFE!**

...ALTHOUGH THERE MIGHT BE AN EMOTIONAL COST I HADN'T CONSIDERED.

151

CATFIGHT!

...AND THEIR BIG OFF-SEASON MOVE WAS SIGNING RON ARTEST. HE'S DEFINITELY GOING TO IMPROVE THEIR DEFENCE.

PLUS, THEY'VE STILL GOT TRACY McGRADY, WHO CAN SCORE FROM ANYWHERE. THE GUY'S A TOTAL ANIMAL.

...BUT ULTIMATELY, IT ALL COMES DOWN TO THE BIG FELLA. IF HIS FOOT IS COMPLETELY HEALED, THE ROCKETS CAN DOMINATE THE NBA.

THIS CONCLUDES MY REPORT ON THE MING DYNASTY.

YOW.

NATE WRIGHT, SUPERBLOGGER

MR ROSA! HOW COME YOU'RE EATING IN HERE INSTEAD OF THE FACULTY LOUNGE?

OH, I JUST NEEDED SOME SOLITUDE, NATE.

WHEN YOU'RE A TEACHER, YOU LEARN TO TREASURE THOSE FEW PRECIOUS MOMENTS WHEN YOU'RE ENTIRELY, COMPLETELY ALONE!

AH. I HEAR YA. I HEAR YA.

ANYWAY, WANNA PLAY "HANGMAN"?

DOOR. SHOULD HAVE LOCKED DOOR.

© 2008 by NEA, Inc.

MR ROSA, CAN I ASK YOU A QUESTION?

OF COURSE, NATE! THAT'S WHAT I'M HERE FOR!

CLASSROOM TEACHING IS ONLY **PART** OF WHAT I DO! I ALSO PROVIDE **GUIDANCE** FOR STUDENTS WHO MIGHT NEED A HELPING HAND!

SO, YES! ASK! ASK AWAY! I CAN'T PROMISE I'LL HAVE ALL THE ANSWERS, BUT I CAN AT LEAST BE A SOUNDING BOARD FOR WHATEVER ISSUE YOU'RE DEALING WITH!

© 2008 by NEA, Inc.

YOU GONNA FINISH THOSE CHIPS?

MR CHUNG, CAN I INTERVIEW YOU FOR MY BLOG?

BLOG?

IT'S CALLED "CLASSROOM CHATTER"! EVERY FEW WEEKS I PROFILE A DIFFERENT TEACHER! YOU KNOW, YOUR LIKES, DISLIKES, HOBBIES...

FWIP!

THANK YOU FOR ASKING, NATE, BUT I PREFER TO KEEP MY PRIVATE LIFE PRIVATE!

my private life private," he said mysteriously, casting furtive glances around the classroom as if trying to hide som

STOP TYPING, SON.

TIK TAK TIK TIKKA TAKKA TIK TAKKA TAK

© 2008 by NEA, Inc.

YOU KNOW, WHEN I GOT MR CHUNG FOR SOCIAL STUDIES, I THOUGHT HE WAS GOING TO BE **COOL**!

...BUT NOW ALL HE DOES IS **YELL** AT ME!

AND WHAT DOES THAT TELL YOU?

IT TELLS ME THAT MR CHUNG HAS EMOTIONAL PROBLEMS.

...OR MAYBE THAT I SHOULDN'T HAVE WRITTEN A LIMERICK ABOUT HIM ON MY BLOG.

PROBABLY A COMBINATION OF THE TWO.

I'M TORN, MR ROSA. ON ONE HAND, I'M TIRED OF THIS PLACE AND I'M READY TO GO BACK TO P.S. 38.

...BUT GOING BACK TO P.S. 38 MEANS I'LL HAVE SOCIAL STUDIES WITH **MRS GODFREY** AGAIN, AND MRS GODFREY IS A BIG, FAT **HORROR SHOW!**

SO, YOU SEE MY DILEMMA.

VIVIDLY.

GAH! I CAN ALMOST SMELL THAT SKUNKY **PERFUME** OF HERS!

© 2008 by NEA, Inc.

Z

HI!

HMN?

I'LL TAKE A CARICATURE!

RIGHT...OK..

CARICATURE by Nate

...AND CAN YOU DRAW ME RIDING A HORSE?

SURE, I GUESS I.... HMM....

CARICATURES by Nate ONLY $2.50

UH... Y'KNOW WHAT? I WAS HAVING A LITTLE NAP JUST NOW AND MY... WELL, MY HAND IS ALL WEAK AND TINGLY.

SHAKE SHAKE SHAKE

11/23

SO WHAT? JUST DRAW!

BUT... MY HAND! I CAN BARELY HOLD THE PENCIL!

LOOK, YOUR SIGN SAYS "CARICATURES," SO **MAKE** ME ONE!

OK..

GRUNT

P O W!

THERE'S A LESSON HERE SOMEWHERE ABOUT THE HAZARDS OF SLEEPING ON THE JOB, BUT MY HEAD HURTS TOO MUCH TO THINK ABOUT IT.

Peirce

© 2008 by NEA, Inc.

NATE'S "FIRST" THANKSGIVING

MR CHUNG, INSTEAD OF **WRITING** MY REPORT ON THE FIRST THANKSGIVING, CAN I DO IT IN COMIC BOOK FORMAT?

HM. I DON'T KNOW, NATE.

PLEASE? PLEEEEEZ? I'VE DONE **OTHER** REPORTS THAT WAY! MRS GODFREY LETS ME DO IT **ALL THE TIME!**

WHOA. HOLD IT. I JUST... ✳KOFF!✳... I JUST USED **MRS GODFREY** AS AN EXAMPLE OF THE WAY A TEACHER SHOULD DO THINGS!

© 2008 by NEA, Inc.

FEELING QUEASY... CALL THE SCHOOL NURSE...

...OR PERHAPS THE DRAMA TEACHER.

MR CHUNG GAVE MY REPORT ON THE FIRST THANKSGIVING A SOLID "B"!

HE SAID HE LOVED THE WAY I DID IT IN COMICS STYLE!

WELL, IF HE WAS SO CRAZY ABOUT IT, WHY DIDN'T HE GIVE YOU AN "A"?

HE TOOK OFF SOME POINTS FOR HISTORICAL ACCURACY.

APPARENTLY HE HAD A PROBLEM WITH THE MIXED MARTIAL ARTS SCENE.

TEACHERS ARE SO PICKY.

WOW! DAD! IT ACTUALLY SEEMS **NORMAL** IN HERE!

WELL, WHY **WOULDN'T** IT?

BECAUSE YOU ALWAYS MANAGE TO **SCREW UP** THANKSGIVING DINNER SOMEHOW! COULD IT BE THAT THIS YEAR YOU'VE FINALLY GOT IT **RIGHT?**

I MEAN, LOOK AT **THIS!** YOU EVEN MADE **STUFF-ING!**

THAT'S GRAVY.

© 2008 by NEA, Inc.

11 27

OH.

THIS IS STUFFING!

OH, THE PAIN!

OK, DAD, HERE'S THE PLAY: YOU'RE GOING TO SPRINT TO THE HYDRANGEA BUSH, THEN CUT ACROSS THE MIDDLE...

AT THAT POINT, YOU'LL TRIP OVER YOUR OWN FEET AND GO SPRAWLING TO THE GROUND, ROLLING AROUND AND SCREAMING, "OH, THE PAIN! THE **PAIN!!**"

YOU'LL THEN CRAWL INSIDE AND SPEND THE REST OF THE WEEKEND ON THE COUCH WITH AN ICE PACK AND A HEATING PAD.

11/29

YOU THROW OUT YOUR BACK A COUPLE TIMES, AND THEY NEVER LET YOU FORGET IT.

HIKE.

© 2008 by NEA, Inc.

THE MEANING
OF WOOF

IT'S DECEMBER, DAD.

THAT IT IS.

...WHICH MEANS IT'S NOW OFFICIALLY OK FOR ME TO DROP HINTS ABOUT WHAT I WANT FOR CHRISTMAS!

AND HERE'S HINT NUMBER ONE!... READY, DAD? DAD!... READY?...

"WOOF"!

12/1

WOOF! GET IT, DAD? WOOF!

COULD BE A LONG MONTH.

ACCORDING TO YOUR LIST, DAD, YOU'D LIKE A BELT, A BOOK OF CROSSWORDS, AND A BATHROBE FOR CHRISTMAS.

RIGHT.

OK! I HEREBY PROMISE TO GIVE YOU ONE OF THOSE ITEMS!

HA!

"HA"?

THAT MEANS YOU HAVE TO GIVE ME AN ITEM FROM MY LIST! FAIR'S FAIR!

12. 4

© 2008 by NEA, Inc.

A SAINT BERNARD, A GREAT DANE, AND A HI-DEF PLASMA T.V.

I PRIORITISED THEM, BUT IT'S YOUR CHOICE!

KISS THIS
JOINT GOODBYE!

THIS IS OUR LAST WEEK AT JEFFERSON!

IT IS?

WHO SAYS?

BUS

THE **NEWSPAPER** SAYS! I JUST READ THE STORY THAT P.S. 38 IS RE-OPENING!

I READ THE NEWS-PAPER, TOO, AND **I** DIDN'T SEE IT!

12/8

IT WAS THE **FRONT PAGE HEADLINE!**

OH. WELL, NO WONDER.

© 2008 by NEA, Inc.

I GO SPORTS, COMICS, JUMBLE.

I GO SUDOKU, SPORTS, DEAR ABBY!

PRINCIPAL NICHOLS, SINCE WE'LL BE GOING BACK TO OUR OWN SCHOOL NEXT WEEK, I THINK WE SHOULD FIND A WAY TO THANK OUR FRIENDS HERE AT JEFFERSON!

CAN WE LEAVE THEM SOME KIND OF SOUVENIR? SOMETHING TO REMIND THEM OF THE TIME WE SPENT HERE?

WHAT A FINE IDEA, NATE! WHAT DID YOU HAVE IN MIND?

☆AHEM!☆

NO.

HEY, MR CHUNG, THEY CLEANED UP THE MOULD AT P.S. 38! WE'RE GOING BACK!

THAT'S WHAT I HEAR!

WELL, NICE KNOWING YOU! SEE YOU AROUND!

UH... HOLD ON, NATE.

YOU'RE NOT GOING BACK TO P.S. 38 UNTIL **MONDAY**! TODAY IS **THURSDAY**!

BUT I NEED TIME TO TRAN-SITION.

RIGHT. TRANSITION OVER TO YOUR SEAT.

© 2008 by NEA, Inc.

SO THEY'VE FINISHED CLEANING UP THE MOULD AT YOUR SCHOOL, EH?

GUESS SO.

YOU KIDS ARE LUCKY EVERYONE'S SO HEALTH-CONSCIOUS NOWADAYS! NOBODY KNEW ANYTHING ABOUT TOXIC MOULD WHEN **I** WAS YOUR AGE!

✳CHUCKLE!✳ WE WERE PROBABLY EXPOSED TO ALL **KINDS** OF HARMFUL AND POISONOUS... UH... POISONOUS...

© 2008 by NEA, Inc.

THAT COULD EXPLAIN A FEW THINGS.

WAIT, WHAT WAS I TALKING ABOUT?

"SHOPPING CONSULTANT"?

THAT'S ME! I HELP FOLKS FIND THE PERFECT HOLIDAY GIFT!

TALK TO ME! I'M A SHOPPING CONSULTANT

SO YOU CAN HELP ME FIND A CHRISTMAS PRESENT FOR A GIRL?

AH! A **SPECIAL** GIRL?

RIGHT. JENNY. BUT UNFORTUNATELY, SHE'S GOING OUT WITH **ARTUR** RIGHT NOW.

...SO I CAN'T GIVE HER SOME CHEESY **ROMANTIC** GIFT. THAT WOULD SEEM SORT OF WEIRD, Y'KNOW.

BUT I DON'T WANT TO GIVE HER A "JUST FRIENDS" GIFT BECAUSE THEN SHE WON'T KNOW I STILL **LIKE** HER!

...SO WHAT I NEED IS A GIFT THAT'LL MAKE JENNY REALISE SHE SHOULD **DUMP** ARTUR AND GET ON BOARD THE NATE LOVE TRAIN.

I'VE GOT... LET'S SEE... ONE DOLLAR AND SIXTY-THREE CENTS.

© 2008 by NEA, Inc.

WORK WITH ME.

YOU KNOW WHAT, IT'S TIME FOR MY LUNCH BREAK...

HOW BAD CAN IT BE?

FOR THE FIRST TIME IN MY LIFE, I'M ACTUALLY LOOKING **FORWARD** TO SCHOOL!

I WAS AWAKE ALL NIGHT THINKING ABOUT...

...THE BOOK REPORT THAT'S DUE TODAY?

BUZZ KILLER.

HM?

WAIT. BOOK WHAT?

SCHOOL PICTURE GUY! HOW COME **YOU'RE** HERE?

TO DOCUMENT THE GRAND REOPENING OF P.S. 38, OF COURSE!

MY TASK: TO CAPTURE THE GLORIOUS MOMENT WHEN THEY CUT THE CEREMONIAL RIBBON, USHERING IN A NEW ERA IN THE SCHOOL'S HISTORY!

SNIP!

CLAP CLAP
CLAP CLAP
CLAP CLAP
CLAP CLAP

© 2008 by NEA, Inc.

GOOD LUCK WITH THAT.

EGAD!

COME ON IN, EVERY-
ONE! WELCOME BACK
TO P.S. 38!

SO ALL
THE MOULD
IS GONE?

YES INDEED, NATE! WE
HAVE NEW CARPETING,
FRESHLY PAINTED WALLS...

WHOA, WHOA!
PAINTED
WALLS?
WHICH
WALLS?

WELL... **ALL** OF THEM!

NO...
NO!...

© 2008 by NEA, Inc.

12
17

NO!

HIS
GRAFFITI
PROJECT
IN THE
THIRD
FLOOR
BATH-
ROOM
WAS ONLY
HALF
DONE.

HOLY **COW! LOOK** AT THIS PLACE!

FORGET ABOUT **LOOKING** AT IT! **SMELL** IT!

IT DOESN'T SMELL ALL MUSTY AND MILDEWY ANYMORE! IT SMELLS **CLEAN!** IT SMELLS **FRESH!**

...AND YET THERE REMAINS AN UNDENIABLE STENCH.

12/18

※GRUMBLE...※

WHAT'S WITH **YOU**, NATE?

MRS GODFREY! CAN YOU **BELIEVE** HER?

WHO ELSE BUT **HER** WOULD SPRING A **POP QUIZ** ON THE LAST DAY OF SCHOOL BEFORE **VACATION**?

WHAT A JERKY THING TO DO! SHE'S NUMBER ONE ON MY JERK LIST!

WHAT'S THE BIG DEAL? I MEAN, THE QUIZ WAS SO **EASY**!

PLUS, SHE'S GRADING IT ON A **CURVE**!

RIGHT! SO UNLESS YOU'RE AT THE VERY **BOTTOM** OF THE CURVE, YOU'LL...

※MMPH!※

OH. ※SNORT!※ RIGHT.

NEVERRR MINNND!

SHE'S JUST BEEN BUMPED DOWN TO NUMBER THREE.

HA HA HEH HEH

HA HA HA

HA HEH

HA

© 2008 by NEA, Inc.

HOUSE
GUEST PEST

TED, WHAT ARE YOU **DOING** HERE?

WELL, MOTHER AND FATHER, FOR SOME REASON, SASHAYED OFF TO **FLORIDA** FOR CHRISTMAS!

SO THERE I WAS, LEFT BEHIND AT YE OLDE HOMESTEAD, FACING THE UNPALATABLE PROSPECT OF SPENDING THE HOLIDAYS **ALONE!**

IT WAS **THEN**, DEAR BROTHER, THAT I REMEMBERED THE GENEROUS INVITATION YOU MADE TO ME LAST SUMMER!

12/23

I SAID, "SEE YOU LATER"!

EX**ACT**LY! AND HERE I AM!

HERE YOU GO, ELLEN! AND NATE, THIS ONE LOOKS LIKE IT'S FOR YOU!

OH **HO!** THAT ONE'S FROM **ME**, NEPHEW O' MINE!

IT'S... WAIT, WHAT IS IT?

IT'S AN **ALBUM**, M'BOY! A **RECORD!**

CLASSIC VINYL IS FAR SUPERIOR TO THE ANTI-SEPTIC SOUND OF CDS OR MP3S! **HONOUR** THE MUSIC! **REBEL** AGAINST TECHNOLOGY!

YOU'RE SAYING, "REBEL AGAINST TECHNOLOGY"?

BUT YOU'RE PLANNING TO HAVE YOUR HEAD CRYO-OGENICALLY FROZEN.

THIS IS DIFFERENT, LAD. THIS IS NEIL DIAMOND.

Peirce

NO MORE
MONOPOLY

WE PLAY MONOPOLY EVERY NEW YEAR'S EVE!

AH! SO I'VE BECOME PART OF A GLORIOUS **TRADITION!**

RIGHT! AND SPEAKING OF TRADITION, I'M ALWAYS THE TOP HAT!

SORRY, DEAR NEPHEW... I'VE ALREADY CHOSEN THE TOP HAT.

WHA-? THE TOP HAT'S MY **LUCKY PIECE!**

I HEREBY CLAIM IT BASED ON FAMILY SENIORITY.

12/30

© 2008 by NEA, Inc.

THAT'S WHAT YOU SAID WHEN YOU ATE ALL THE "VIENNA FINGERS"!

HERE, YOU BE THE THIMBLE. THE THIMBLE IS SOMEWHAT HATLIKE.

Peirce

UNCLE TED, I'LL TRADE YOU MARVIN GARDENS FOR NEW YORK AVENUE!

MARVIN GARDENS, YOU SAY? I THINK **NOT!**

THE NAME "MARVIN" CONJURES UP TRAUMATIC MEMORIES OF A **BULLY** NAMED MARVIN WHO USED TO **TORMENT** ME WHEN I WAS YOUNGER!

THE HORRIBLE DAY WHEN HE SMASHED MY "THUNDERCATS" LUNCHBOX AGAINST A WALL IS INDELIBLY **SEARED** INTO MY **BRAIN!**

THIS IS THE WEIRDEST GAME OF MONOPOLY OF ALL TIME.

HIGH SCHOOL CAN BE NASTY, LADS. RE-MEMBER THAT.

...AND THAT CONCLUDES OUR DISCUSSION OF WHY THE ORANGE PROPERTIES ARE THE BEST ECONOMIC VALUE ON THE ENTIRE BOARD!

Z...

GREAT **SCOTT**! I COMPLETELY LOST TRACK OF THE **TIME**! IT'S ALMOST **MIDNIGHT**! THE NEW YEAR IS **NIGH**!

YA GOTTA H

IS EVERYONE READY FOR THE BIG MOMENT? DOES EVERYONE HAVE A NEW YEAR'S RESOLUTION READY TO ANNOUNCE?

I RESOLVE TO NEVER PLAY MONOPOLY WITH YOUR UNCLE AGAIN.

LET'S ALL SING "AULD LANG SYNE"! I'LL GET MY ACCORDION!

MAKE IT
OR BREAK IT

$\frac{1}{7}$

PET NAMES

WHAT A PRETTY FACE!

Nate's dad has framed some of Nate's self-portraits. Draw yourself doing the same things as Nate!

RHYTHM & RHYME

A picture is worth a thousand words. Fill in these limerick poems and create your own, all inspired by Nate's Sunday strip art!

Nate is a pretty swell guy
But one day a ball flew into his _____.
It made him quite sad,
Though he couldn't get _____,
He did yell "Why, ball, _____?!"

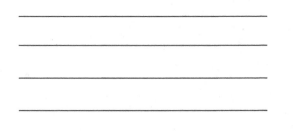

Francis loves to read most of all
Even on a wave standing _____.
I'd be willing to bet
(If the book didn't get _____)
He wouldn't notice a _____!

AWESOME ANNOUNCEMENTS

Have you suffered through those BOOORING announcements at school? What would you say if you had the microphone? Change it up and shout out something FUN!

Every day is a
snow day!

Nate loves Jenny!

The lasagna smells
like old socks!

NATE ≠ NEAT

Have you ever scrambled the letters in your name to see if they spell anything else? Well, **I** have. And guess what: MY letters spell **N·E·A·T!**

KSSSCH!

Pretty ironic, right? Hey, I realise I'm not exactly Joe Tidy. **EVERYBODY** knows it. But that doesn't stop Francis, who colour-codes his underwear, from pointing it out about a jillion times a day.

Your desk is **DISGUSTING**. You have paint on your shirt. Oh, and you have Cheez Doodle stains all over your face. What a SLOB you are!

Francis has been telling me to clean up my act since I poured applesauce down his pants back in kindergarten. Of course, I've always ignored him. But then last week my sloppiness got Francis in trouble... and he **NEVER** gets in trouble!

I felt so bad about it, I decided to actually try to get neater. And thanks to

I'm **VERY** disappointed in you.

Oops.

Teddy and his uncle Pedro, the hypnotist, it's working... **TOO** well. All of the sudden, I'm starting to act **JUST LIKE FRANCIS!** Frankly, I think I'm losing my mind.

You're doing **GREAT!**

I'm **FLIPPIN' OUT!**

What a **MESS!**
Read all about it in
BIG NATE FLIPS OUT!!

Lincoln Peirce

(pronounced "purse") is a cartoonist/writer and *New York Times* bestselling author of the hilarious Big Nate book series (www.bignatebooks.com), now published in twenty-five countries worldwide. He is also the creator of the comic strip *Big Nate*, which appears in over two hundred and fifty U.S. newspapers and online daily at www.bignate.com. Lincoln's boyhood idol was Charles Schulz of *Peanuts* fame, but his main inspiration for Big Nate has always been his own experience as a sixth grader. Just like Nate, Lincoln loves comics, ice hockey and Cheez Doodles (and dislikes cats, figure skating and egg salad). His Big Nate books have been featured on *Good Morning America* and in *USA Today*, the *Washington Post*, and the *Boston Globe*. He has also written for Cartoon Network and Nickelodeon. Lincoln lives with his wife and two children in Portland, Maine.

GINA RATES ALL THE BIG NATE BOOKS!

Grade: **A+**

Comments: Nate Wright gets detention all day? I approve!

Grade: **A++**

Comments: As far as I'm concerned, I'm the hero here.

Grade: **A+**

Comments: Like doing extra-credit assignments... my dream come true!